LESLEY GARRETT
SONG COLLECTION
Favourite songs for soprano and piano

Cover photography: Sheila Rock. Styling: Daniela Agnelli.
Make-up: Tony James. Hair: Trevor Sorbie.

© BMG Entertainment International UK and Ireland Limited. All rights reserved.
Music setting by Barnes Music Engraving.
Printed in Great Britain by Caligraving Limited, Thetford, Norfolk.

Chester Music
(A division of Music Sales Limited)
8/9 Frith Street, London W1V 5TZ.

BIOGRAPHY

Lesley Garrett is Britain's most popular soprano, regularly appearing in both opera and in concert, on television and disc; she has won both critical acclaim and the affection of many fans and music lovers.

As a recording artist, Lesley has seven solo CDs to her credit, from which this book has been selected: *Diva! A Soprano At The Movies*, *Prima Donna*, *Simple Gifts*, *Soprano In Red*, *Soprano In Hollywood*, *A Soprano Inspired* and *Lesley Garrett*. The songs in this book include Lesley's favourites and those most requested by her fans. The incredible popularity of these CDs is reflected in the numerous gold and silver discs they have received; *Soprano In Hollywood* has also been awarded the Gramophone Award for 'Best-selling Classical Artist of the Year'. Lesley is an exclusive BMG recording artist.

After studying for six years at the Royal Academy of Music in London, of which she is now a Fellow, Lesley Garrett won the prestigious Decca-Kathleen Ferrier Memorial Competition in 1979, and the Countess of Munster Award. She completed her education at the National Opera Studio and continues to work with her singing teacher, Joy Mammen. Lesley's operatic career included early engagements at the Wexford Festival, Welsh National Opera, Opera North, the Buxton Festival and Glyndebourne Festival Opera, before joining English National Opera in 1984. Her repertoire includes Mozart's *Zaide*, Susanna in *The Marriage Of Figaro*, Despina in *Così Fan Tutte*, Caroline in Cimarosa's *The Secret Marriage*, Atalanta in *Xerxes*, Eurydice in *Orpheus In The Underworld* and Bella in Tippett's *Midsummer Marriage*. Lesley continues to work regularly with ENO, and she has recently been appointed a member of the Board of Directors. In 1998 she was also invited to become a Trustee of the National Foundation for Youth Music, established by the Department of Culture, Media and Sport.

Determined to make opera accessible to all, Lesley has won fans around the world through her wide-ranging appearances and repertoire, from open-air gala concerts to sold-out nationwide tours and concerts at the Royal Albert Hall. She is in increasing demand internationally following her USA debut in 1995, which was followed by three concerts of excerpts from *My Fair Lady* at the Hollywood Bowl with Jonathan Pryce.

Lesley's popularity has extended to an even greater audience through numerous television appearances, including her own *Lesley Garrett… Tonight!* series, which attracted an audience of over three million views for each show. Lesley was also the subject of a South Bank Show on LWT in November 1998.

INTRODUCTORY NOTES

Giulio Caccini, who was born in or near Rome around the year 1545 and was buried in Florence in 1618, was one of the composers most closely associated with the beginnings around 1600 of the new form of opera and with the development of the Baroque style. He was a singer of note – a tenor – who would have performed his own compositions in the new idiom. The present arrangement of his *Ave Maria* was created in recent times, rather in the way in which a fragment of an Adagio by Albinoni evolved into a world-famous piece in the hands of a musicologist after the Second World War. In this form, the *Ave Maria* has been widely taken up.

Georges Bizet's *Carmen* of 1875 has long been the world's most popular opera, and with its vivid colour, dramatic plot and immediate melodies it was only a matter of time before someone decided to adapt it as a musical. Enter Oscar Hammerstein II, lyricist of a host of successful shows written in collaboration with Richard Rodgers, who in 1943 produced *Carmen Jones* on Broadway. It was a huge success and was later made into a Hollywood film. In this version, Carmen Jones works in a parachute factory supplying a US airbase in the south, and at the beginning of the second scene, set in Billy Pastor's café, Bizet's gypsy song is jazzed up into *Beat Out Dat Rhythm on a Drum*.

Rimsky-Korsakov wrote fifteen operas, many of them drawing on Russian legends and fairy-tales. *Sadko* (1898) took as its hero a folk singer whose adventures on and even under the sea bring him and his home city of Novgorod permanent prosperity. In the final scene, the Sea King's favourite daughter, Volkhova, sings a lullaby (*Berceuse*) to the sleeping Sadko, with whom she has fallen in love.

Carl Zeller (1842-98) was one of the minor masters of Viennese light music, who found time amidst a career in the Austrian civil service to compose a sequence of operettas as well as songs and choral works. Of these the most famous is *The Bird Seller*, still frequently performed today. But also of note was his *Der Obersteiger* ('The Mine Foreman') of 1894, remembered for its winsome song *Don't Be Cross*, originally sung by the tenor hero in the form of a parable about a fisherman rejected by a mill girl who later has the tables turned on her.

Léo Delibes is best known for his ballets *Coppélia* and *Sylvia* and for his opera *Lakmé*, set in British India, which includes the famous soprano showpiece called the Bell Song and a wonderful duet made famous in a recent advertising campaign. Like many French composers of his time, Delibes had a great gift for melody and colour, and his song *Les Filles de Cadix* shows the same delight in seductive Spanish rhythms as his friend Georges Bizet's *Carmen*.

It was George Bernard Shaw's witty comedy *Pygmalion* – about Eliza Doolittle, a flower-girl from Covent Garden with a gorblimey accent who is transformed into a queen of society by Professor Higgins, an expert in phonetics – that formed the basis of the Lerner and Loewe hit musical *My Fair Lady* of 1956. The show was later turned into a Hollywood film and has even entered the repertory of German opera houses. As Higgins's often impatient teaching begins to bear fruit, Eliza is thrilled at her ability to flaunt herself in high society, as she makes clear in *I Could Have Danced All Night*.

Emmanuel Chabrier (1841-94) was a career civil servant with a post in the French Ministry of the Interior who eventually gave up his day job to concentrate on his first love, music. Even before taking this fatal step in 1880, however, he had produced a couple of lighter works for the theatre, including the opéra-bouffe *L'Etoile* ('The Star'), which recent productions have shown to be a particularly stylish piece. The setting is the court of King Ouf I, monarch of the thirty six realms, who has the unfortunate habit of executing people as a way of celebrating his birthday… Unaware of what lies in store for him, the handsome young pedlar Lazuli introduces himself to the audience in *I'm Called Lazuli*.

Cervantes' knightly hero Don Quixote has inspired many compositions since his appearance in one of the greatest works of Spanish literature in the early seventeenth century, including a suite by Telemann, a symphonic poem by Richard Strauss and an opera by Massenet. Among more recent treatments, the American musical *Man of La Mancha* by Joe Darion and Mitch Leigh was first produced in 1965 and won worldwide success on the commercial stage. The sad but idealistic hero goes through various adventures, maintaining his courtly behaviour sometimes at the cost of his dignity, but always continuing to dream his impossible dream.

Rinaldo (1711) was not only George Frideric Handel's first opera written for London, but also the first Italian opera composed for the British capital. Its huge success led to the German-born composer settling in Britain and addressing himself thereafter to the British public. The opera's setting is the Holy Land at the time of the First Crusade (1096-9), when the Christian knight Rinaldo has to struggle against magical as well as human foes. The aria *Lascia ch'io pianga* ('Let me weep') is sung by his beloved Almirena at a point when she is held captive by the enemy.

Albert Hay Malotte (1895-1964) was an American composer and pianist who wrote music for Walt Disney cartoons, two ballets, choral pieces and songs, but it is his setting of *The Lord's Prayer* that has won him immortality. Its first performer was the Ukrainian-born baritone Igor Gorin, who at first refused to sing it (he was a Jew, and highly religious) but eventually relented. With just a couple of radio airings, the piece took off, quickly becoming the most popular item in Gorin's repertoire.

Franz Lehár's operettas are the treasures of what has been called the 'Silver Age' of operetta. One of the later examples is *Paganini* (1925), a fictionalised account of the life and loves of the legendary violinist that was written for the great Austrian tenor Richard Tauber. In *Love, Live Forever* – made famous on the London stage by the great musical comedy star Evelyn Laye – Paganini's beloved, Princess Maria Anna Elisa of Lucca, reacts defiantly to the fact that her beloved violinist has been ordered to leave town because of their scandalous relationship.

The English composer Geoffrey Burgon achieved fame with his music for a highly acclaimed BBC television series of 1979 starring Sir Alec Guinness and based on John Le Carré's espionage novel *Tinker, Tailor, Soldier, Spy*. In the book, Guinness's character George Smiley, called in to investigate a mole in the British secret service, longs to retire – hence the suitability of the text of the Nunc dimittis, a part of the Anglican service of Evensong: 'Lord, now lettest thou thy servant depart in peace'.

Puccini composed just one comedy – *Gianni Schicchi* – which formed the final part of his 'triptych' of three one-act operas and was first performed at the Metropolitan in New York in 1918. Its central character is a wily peasant brought in by a wealthy Florentine family to help them circumvent the will of their recently deceased relative. His daughter Lauretta, however, has fallen in love with a young member of that family, despite the fact that his elders and betters consider her beneath them. Gianni Schicchi is outraged at this, and threatens to leave them to their own devices, but Lauretta pleads with him in her famous aria *O mio babbino caro* to help her marry the man she loves.

As a master of operetta who had also had aspirations as a 'serious' composer, Franz Lehár was no doubt delighted to be asked to write a work for the august Vienna State Opera itself. The result was *Giuditta*, a large-scale piece premiered with Jarmila Novotná in the title role and – inevitably – with Richard Tauber as the young officer who falls for her charms. The first performance in 1934 was the last appearance of a new stage work by the composer. Among its highlights is *On My Lips Every Kiss Is Like Wine*, sung by Giuditta in Scene 4, by which point she is a cabaret artist in a North African night-club.

The Shakers were a religious community founded in England by the visionary Ann Lee who then led them to America in 1774. The last Shaker, Ethel Hudson, died as recently as 1992. Among the sect's observances was a kind of ecstatic dancing that gave them their name, and part of their musical heritage is an unforgettable tune known as *Simple Gifts* which Aaron Copland used in his ballet *Appalachian Spring*, and Sidney Carter made popular in his song *Lord of the Dance*.

Roberta (also known as *Gowns by Roberta*) received its Broadway launch in 1933, and was one of a long series of shows in which Jerome Kern demonstrated his immense distinction as a composer of popular song. In the subsequent screen version (starring Fred Astaire and Ginger Rogers), Irene Dunne sang *Smoke Gets in Your Eyes* – she is a former Russian princess working as a designer in the Parisian fashion house of Roberta. Kern's wonderful melody, however, had a longer history, beginning life as a signature tune for a radio series before being briefly co-opted into *Show Boat*.

Tosca, first performed in 1900, remains one of Puccini's best-loved scores and is the classic example of a thriller in opera. The police chief Baron Scarpia's amorous pursuit of the singer Floria Tosca will lead eventually to his own death (at her hands) as well as that of her lover Cavaradossi and Tosca herself. In the second act, the dramatic highlight of the piece, Scarpia presents Tosca with a terrible dilemma: he will save the life of the condemned Cavaradossi, but only if Tosca allows him to make love to her. In her famous aria *Vissi d'arte*, Tosca asks God why he has allowed such suffering to come upon her.

Mozart's *The Marriage of Figaro* (1786) is a perfect comedy in opera, in which the complexities of the characters' emotional involvements are detailed in music of supreme subtlety and elegance. Cherubino is the young pageboy of the aristocratic Almaviva household, experiencing for the first time emotional feelings that he can barely understand, let alone control. In *Voi che sapete*, sung to the Countess and her maid Susanna, he asks them to explain to him what is going on inside him.

Until his death in 1951, Ivor Novello had been one of the prime movers in the West End theatre – as matinée idol, composer and writer of a sequence of highly successful plays and musical comedies – for more than a quarter of a century. *The Dancing Years* was staged at Drury Lane on the eve of the Second World War and took as its subject a Viennese composer called Rudi Kleber (played by Novello himself) and his love for operetta star Maria Ziegler (played by Mary Ellis). In the first act, Rudi interests Maria in a new waltz he has written, the *Waltz of My Heart*, which she takes up with great enthusiasm.

The Phantom of the Opera, Andrew Lloyd Webber's musical based on the Gothic horror story by Gaston Leroux, began its run at Her Majesty's Theatre in London in 1986 and is still playing fourteen years later. The show's heroine, opera singer Christine Daaé, is pursued and encouraged by the phantom himself – in reality a deformed and embittered composer – but finds herself obliged to assist those wishing to bring him to justice for the crimes he has committed. In her confused state, she visits the grave of her father, her lost guide, and opens her heart to him in *Wishing You Were Somehow Here Again*.

George Hall

Ave Maria

Music by Giulio Caccini. Arranged by Nick Ingman.

a - ve Ma - ri - a. A - ve Ma -

-ri - a, a - ve Ma - ri - a.

A - - - A - - - A -

- - ve Ma - ri - a.

9

-A - - - A - - ve Ma -

-ri - a.

Solo 8va

mp

pp

Beat Out Dat Rhythm on a Drum

(from "Carmen Jones")

Words by Oscar Hammerstein II. Music by Georges Bizet.

Andantino (♩ = 100)

N.B. Begin slowly, and get gradually faster and faster, clear to the end of the number.

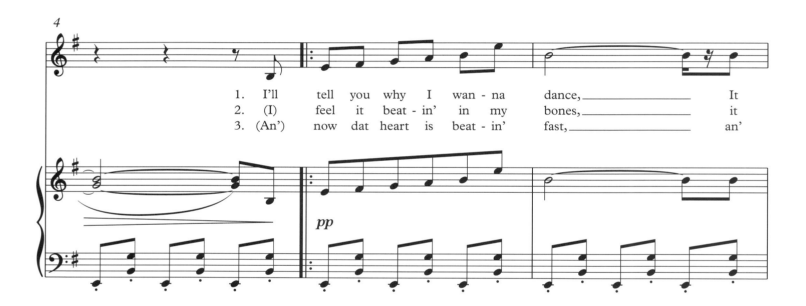

1. I'll tell you why I wan - na dance,_____ It
2. (I) feel it beat - in' in my bones,_____ it
3. (An') now dat heart is beat - in' fast,_____ an'

ain' de sweet-ness in de mu - sic. I like de sweet-ness in de
feels like twen - ty mill - yun tom - toms, I know dere's twen - ty mill - yun
dat's a rhy - thm I kin dance_____ to, I'm might - y glad I got a

mu - sic, But_ dat ain'_ why I wan - na dance!_____
tom - toms Beat-in' 'way down deep in - side my bones!_____
chance____ to, Wid dat one big_ heart dat's beat - in' fast!_____

— It's sump - in' thump-in' in de
— I feel it beat - in' in my
— To - mor - row morn - in' let it

dim. *pp*

bass, A bump-in' un-der-neath de mu - sic, Dat
heart An' den I get a kin' o' dream An'
rain, To - mor - row morn - in' let it pour, To-

13

bum-bum-bump-in' un - der mu — — sic Is__ all I__ need_____ to__ start me__
in my dream it kin' o'   seem_____ Dere's jus' one__ heart__ in__ all de__

3rd Verse

night we's in de groove to - geth — — er, Ain' gon-na wor - ry 'bout storm — y

rit.   a tempo

off.   I don' need no - thin' else to start me off._____
worl'   Dere ain' but one big heart fo' all de worl'._____

weath — er, Gon - na kick ol' trou - ble out de door._____

colla voce

Beat   out   dat   rhy-thm on   a   drum,_____   Beat   out   dat
Beat   out   dat   rhy-thm on   a   drum,_____   Beat   out   dat
Beat   out   ol'   trou-ble on   a   drum,_____   Beat   out   ol'

p sempre più animato

rhy-thm on   a   drum,_____   Beat   out   dat   rhy-thm on   a   drum,   An'
rhy-thm on   a   drum,_____   Beat   out   dat   rhy-thm on   a   drum,   Dere's
trou-ble on   a   drum,_____   Beat   out   ol'   trou-ble on a   drum,   An'

I   don'   need   no   tune   at   all._____   Beat   me   dat
one big   heart fo'   all   de   worl'._____   Beat   out   dat
kick his   car - cass thru   de   door._____   Beat   out   dat

15

rhy-thm on a drum,   Beat me date   rhy-thm on a drum,_____
rhy-thm on a drum,   Beat out dat   rhy-thm on a drum,_____
rhy-thm on a drum,   Beat out dat   rhy-thm on a drum,_____

Beat me dat   rhy-thm on a drum,   An' I don't need no tune at
Beat out dat   rhy-thm on a drum,   Dere's one big heart fo' all de
Beat out dat   rhy-thm on a drum,   An' kick ol' trou-ble out de

all!_____
worl'!_____

2. I door,___ kick 'im out de door!___ Kick 'im out de
3. An'

door!_____ Kick 'im out de door!_____ Kick 'im out de door!_____

BERCEUSE
(FROM "SADKO")

Words and music by Nicolay Rimsky-Korsakov.
English translation by Amanda Holden.

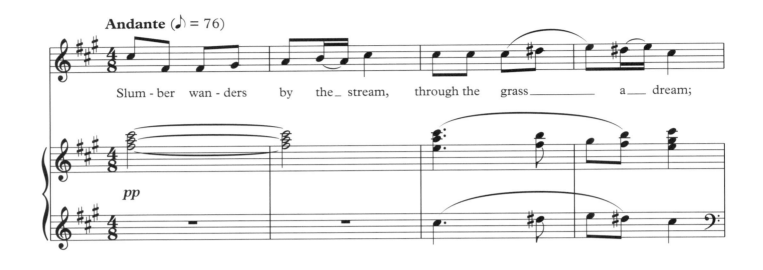

Slum - ber wan - ders by the_ stream, through the grass_____ a__ dream;

and the dream flies_ to and fro, search - ing high_____ and low;

'Tell me what I long to know, tell me where to find Sad - ko!'

Lul - la - by, lul - la - by, lul - la - by, lul - la - by.

'My Sad - ko has laid his__ head on the mea - dow's

fra - grant__ bed, shel - tered in these__ gras - sy bowers

by a ta - pes - try of flowers,' then I soft - ly

sing once more to the he - ro I a - dore;

Lul - la - by, lul - la - by, lul - la - by,

lul - la - by!

20

Shade him in your emer - ald ___ glance, all you sil - ky ___ wa - ter ___ plants; reeds and gras - ses ___ bend with grace, hold him in your ___

soft em - brace; we shall ne - ver

be a - part, his sweet sing - ing

won my heart!

Poco meno mosso

With-in   the morn-ing's ro - sy   glow_____

I   come   to wish you   well,   Sad-ko!

23

For I, the Prin - cess Volk - ho-va, who sees the fu - ture from a-far, will dis - ap - pear in mis - ty light to be a ri - ver, day and night; I'll surge _____ a - cross the mea - dows' reach _____

and down _____ to - wards a gold - en

beach; _____ as-cend the banks so wide and steep, to be be-

-side you as you sleep; I swear, be - lov - ed friend, I'm

faith - ful to the end! _____ Ah, _____ your sing - ing

charms_____ my heart and I'm yours_____ for ev - er . . .

Tempo I (♪ = 126)

G.P.

Lul - la - by, lul - la - by,

lul - la - by, lul - la - by my_____

love!_____

pp trem.

Don't Be Cross

(from "Der Obersteiger")

Words by M. West and L. Held. Music by Carl Zeller.
English translation by Peter Carroll. Arranged by Frank Naylor.

Viennese Waltz Tempo (Allegro)

1. She was a mil - ler's daugh - ter fair,
2. She went in search of wealth and fame;

She had ad - mir - ers ev - 'ry - where,
Some - how the right man ne - ver came,

But   she   loved   best   a   fish -   er   boy,
Then,   when   she   found   her   hopes   were   vain,

and   his   at - ten - tions   she'd   en - joy.
Sad - ly   she   turned   back home   a - gain.

He   could - n't   bear   to   part   from   her,
She   left   her   fool - ish   pride   be - hind,

He   longed   to   give   his   heart   to   her,
Told   her   true   love   she'd   changed   her   mind.

But in her tan - ta - li - sing way,
Asked him to mar - ry her, but he

Laugh - ing - ly she would say;
an - swered her laugh - ing - ly:

Don't be cross now. Don't sit and sigh,

Don't be cross, Don't you see,_____

You are not the one for me.

one for me._____

LES FILLES DE CADIX

Words by Alfred de Musset. Music by Léo Delibes.

Nous ven-ions de voir   le tau-reau,_____ Trois gar-çons, trois fil - let -

Sur la pe - louse il

fai - sait beau,_____ Et nous dans - ions un bo - lé - ro_____ Au son des cas - ta -

avec la voix   *a tempo*

- gnet - - - - tes.

Di - tes-moi, voi - sin, Si j'ai bon - ne mine, Et si ma bas-qui - ne Va bien ce ma - tin.

soutenu

Et nous dan-sions un bo-lé-ro,_____ Un soir, c'é - tait di - man - - - - che._____ Vers nous s'en vint un

I Could Have Danced All Night

(from "My Fair Lady")

Words by Alan Jay Lerner. Music by Frederick Loewe.

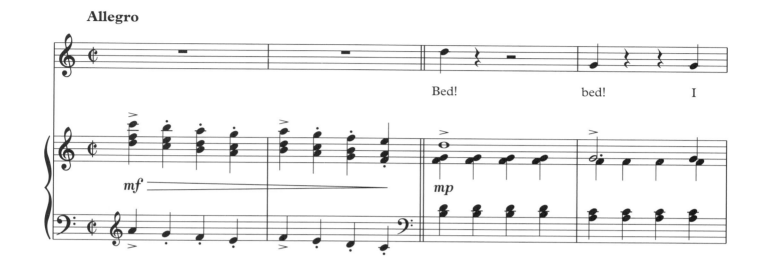

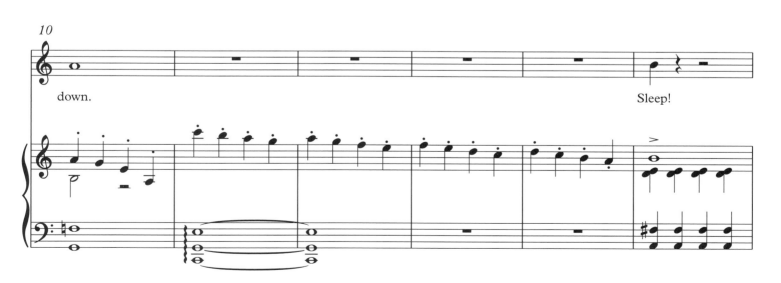

sleep! I could-n't sleep to-night, Not for all the

jew - els in the crown. _____

REFRAIN (*very brightly*)

(1.) I could have danced _____ all night! _____ I could have
(2.) I could have danced all night! _____

danced _____ all night! _____ And still _____
I could have danced all night! _____

42

have begged_____ for more._____
And still have begged for more._____

I could have spread_____ my wings_____
I could have spread my wings_____

And done a thou - sand things_____ I've
And done a thou - sand things_____ I've

nev - er done_____ be - fore._____
I've nev - er done be - fore._____

when he _____ be - gan to dance _____ with

me, _____ I could have danced, danced, danced, _____

All night.   night. _____

I'm Called Lazuli

(from "L'Etoile")

Words by Eugène Leterrier and Albert Vanloo. Music by Emmanuel Chabrier.
English translation by Jeremy Sams.

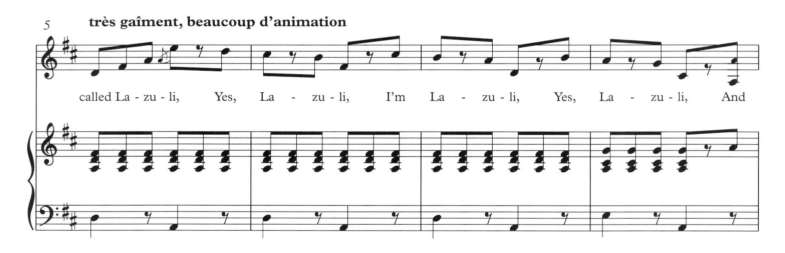

be ex-act I__ am en-gaged to coun-ter-act the ef-fects of age. I

rall.   rit.   a tempo

take them_____ and I make__ them up_____

to per-fec - tion, Make them up to per-fec -

a tempo

-tion. My name is La - zu - li,_____ the la-dies all come to

me, The la - dies come to me, they come to

me, they come to

me.

None of the

never entice enough kisses? I'll tell you precisely why this is; A cake of this, my patent gloss, will make you kiss like candy floss! Your eyes will be dark_ and shady, That's always the mark of a lady. Another simple trick of mine, it's just a stick of five and nine. The

net ef - fect is quite di - vine if the la - dy knows where to draw the line and the whole de - sign is twice as fine as He - len - a Ru - ben - - stein; And if you've got a wrin - kled skin, a wob - bly grin, a dou - ble chin, Just come to me, I'll take you

in. The mo - ther, the daugh - ter, I pro - mise they will seem as one. _____ With my ma - gic wa - ter, No mi - ra - cle that can't be done. Come and take my ad - vice, It is yours at a

price!   Yes, I'm called La - zu - li, And they all come to me, yes they all come to

me.   Ah!   ah!

ah!   ah!

Tempo I vivo

I'm called La - zu - li, Yes, La - zu - li, I'm La - zu - li, Yes,

142 **a tempo vivo**

-tion. My name is La - zu - li,_____ The la - dies all come to

146 **Même mouvt.**

me! The la - dies come to me, they come to me._____

150

They come_____ to me.

154

159

55

The Impossible Dream

(from "Man of La Mancha")

Words by Joe Darion. Music by Mitch Leigh.

Not too slow (Tempo di Bolero)

run_____ where the brave dare not go;_____ To right_____ the un-right-a-ble

wrong,_____ To love,_____ pure and chaste, from a-

-far,_____ To try,_____ when your arms are too

wear-y,_____ To reach_____ the un-reach-a-ble

star! This is my Quest____ to fol-low that star,____ No mat-ter how hope-less,____ no mat-ter how far,____ To fight for the right____ with-out ques-tion or pause,____ To be will-ing to march in-to hell for a hea-ven-ly

cause!_____ And I know,_____ if I'll on-ly be

true_____ to this glor-i-ous Quest,_____ That my

heart_____ will lie peace-ful and calm_____ when I'm laid to my

rest. And the world_____ will be bet-ter for

this,_____ That one man,_____ scorned and cov-ered with scars,_____ Still_

strove,_____ with his last ounce of cour-age,_____ To reach_____ the un-reach-a - ble

stars!_____

Lascia ch'io pianga

(from "Rinaldo")

Words by Giacomo Rossi. Music by George Frideric Handel.

Las - cia ch'io pian - ga mia cru - da sor - te,

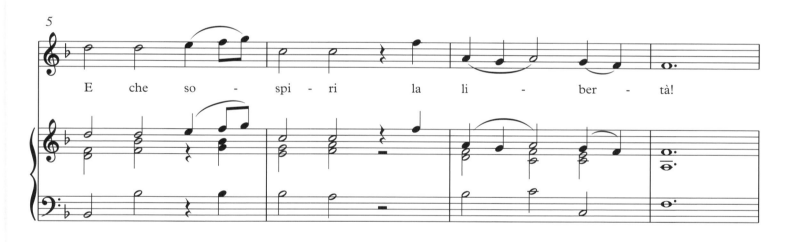

E che so - spi - ri la li - ber - tà!

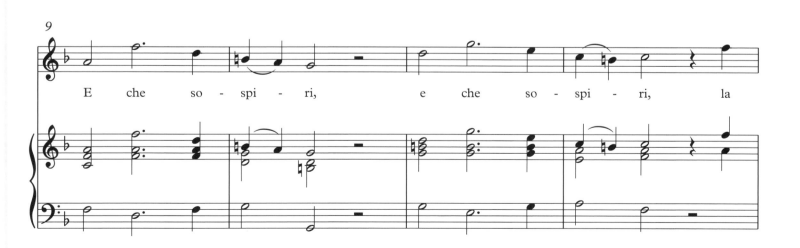

E che so - spi - ri, e che so - spi - ri, la

li - ber - tà! Las - cia ch'io pian - ga

mia cru - da sor - te, E che so -

-spi - ri la li - ber - tà!

The Lord's Prayer

Words from St. Matthew, Ch.6. Music by Albert Hay Malotte.

dai - ly bread. And for - give us our

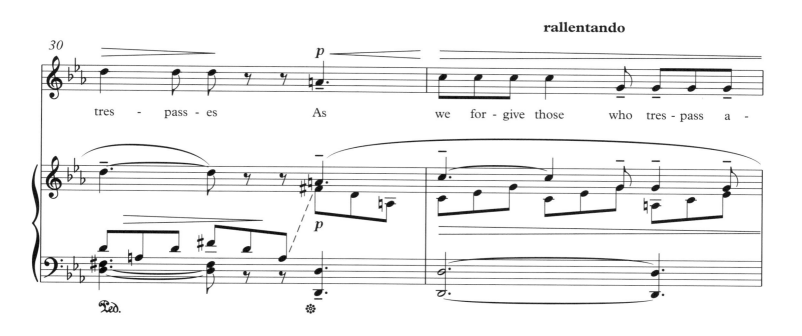

tres - pass - es As we for - give those who tres - pass a -

- gainst us. And

lead us not in - to temp - ta - tion; But de - liv - er us from

Poco meno mosso, e sonoramente

e - vil: For thine is the

king - dom,_____ and the pow - er,_____ and the

glo - ry,_____ for ev - er._____

Tempo I

A - men._____

rallentando e morendo

69

LOVE, LIVE FOREVER

(FROM "PAGANINI")

Words by Paul Knepler & Bela Jenbach. Music by Franz Lehár.
English translation by A.P. Herbert.

Allegretto

Love, to my aid, for I need you now, I *will* have my way, though I know not how The

sun and the moon and the stars com-bine But he's mine, he is *mine.*

Love, life's be-gin-ning and end - ing, Ne -

- ver de - part. Love, from the

Hea - vens des - cend - ing, Rule_____ in my heart._____

poco animato

Love, get - ting or giv - ing,

meno

Makes life worth the liv - ing For where

love has not been What does life *mean?*_____

string

72

Nunc Dimittis
(from "Tinker, Tailor, Soldier, Spy")

Music by Geoffrey Burgon.

O mio babbino caro

(from "Gianni Schicchi")

Words by Giuseppe Adami. Music by Giacomo Puccini.

O mio bab-bi — no ca — ro, mi pia-ce, è bel — lo,

bel — lo: vo 'an — da — re in Por — ta Ros — sa

a com-pe-rar l'a-nel - lo! Sì, sì, ci vo-glio an-

-da - re! E se l'a-mas - si in-dar - no, an-

-drei sul Pon - te Vec - chio, ma per but-tar - mi in

Ar - no! Mi strug - go e mi tor-men - to! O

79

On My Lips Every Kiss Is Like Wine

(from "Giuditta")

Words by Paul Knepler & Fritz Löhner. Music by Franz Lehár.
English translation by Geoffrey Dunn.

there they stand. Their eyes look deep in mine. They al - ways kiss my hand.

Why ev - er should it be, They speak of ma - gic

charms in me That no man can re - sist? For ev - 'ry time they

look at me these charms per - sist. But when the soft lights

rit.

glint and glance As mid-night hours go by,

They hear me sing, they see me dance: It's then that I know

why._____ On my lips ev-'ry kiss is like

wine;_____ In my arms love is more than di-vine._____

a tempo

rit. **Valse moderato**

It's en - graved in the stars high a - bove me;_____ Men must
kiss me,_____ Men must love me._____ When my feet haunt - ing
rhy - thms in - spire,_____ In my eyes gleam the flames of de -
- sire._____ When I dance, then I know Fate's de - sign._____

On my lips ev-'ry kiss is like wine.

I have a dan-cer's blood,

That rules me like a throb-bing flood. My mo-ther was the

danc-ing star With-out a ri-val at the gold-en Al-ca-zar.

How great she must have been! In dreams I have so of - ten seen The rap - tures when she danced; She held each heart en - thralled and ev - 'ry eye en - tranced. Her spi - rit wakes in me a - gain, My for - tune wills it so.

rit.

a tempo

At night I dance as she did then, And this is all I know. On my lips ev - 'ry kiss is like wine; In my arms love is more than di - vine. It's en - graved in the stars high a - bove me; Men must

rit. **Valse moderato** **rit.** **a tempo**

kiss me,_____ Men must love me._____

When I dance, then I know Fate's de - sign._____

_____ On my lips ev - 'ry kiss is like wine._____

SIMPLE GIFTS

Traditional. Additional Words by Fredwyn Hosier.
Arranged by Paul Bateman.

'Tis the gift to be sim-ple 'tis the gift to be free, 'tis the gift to come down where you ought to be and when we find our-selves in the place just right 'twill be in the val-ley of love and de-light.

There's a gift in the mu-sic, there's a gift in the song, that helps us find the place where we be-long, and when we know we've found where we should be then our lives can be lived in___ har - mo - ny. When true sim-

90

-pli - ci - ty is gained to bow and to bend we'll not be ash-amed, to

turn, turn, will be___ our de - light,_____ for in

turn - ing, turn - ing, we come round right._____

Come find a me - lo - dy that's true, weav - ing it's way through all we___ do, to sing, sing will be___ our de - light for with - in the song we___ come round right.___ 'Tis the gift to be sim-ple 'tis the gift to be free, 'tis the

gift to come down where you ought to be, and when we find our-selves in the place just right, 'twill be in the val - ley of love and de - light,_____ de - light.

Smoke Gets in Your Eyes

(from "Roberta")

Words by Otto Harbach. Music by Jerome Kern.

They asked me how I knew my true love was true,_____

_ I of course re - plied, some-thing here in - side can-not be de -

- nied.
They said some-day you'll find all who love are

blind, when your heart's on fire, you must re - a -

- lize smoke gets in your eyes.

So I chaffed them and I gai - ly laughed to think they could

say   "When a love-ly flame dies   smoke gets in your   eyes".

They   said some-day you'll   find   all who love are

blind,_____ when your heart's on fire, you must re - a -

- lize smoke gets in your eyes._____

So I chaffed__ them and I gai - ly laughed__ to think they could doubt my

love. Yet to - day____ my love has flown a - way____ I am with -

-out my love. Now laugh-ing friends de-ride tears I can-not hide, so I smile and say "When a love-ly flame dies, smoke gets in your eyes".

Vissi d'arte
(from "Tosca")

Words by Luigi Illica & Giuseppe Giacosa. Music by Giacomo Puccini.

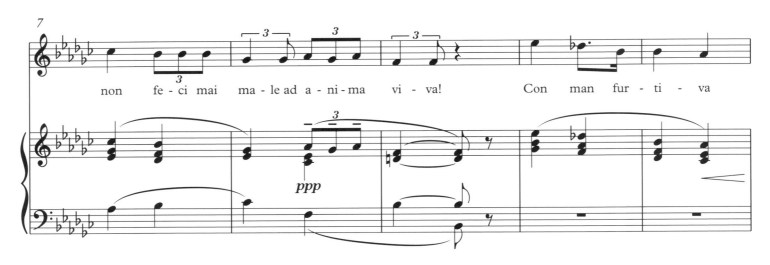

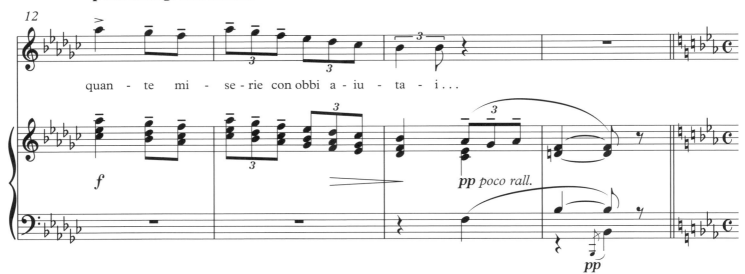

Sem - pre_____ con fè_ sin - ce - ra la mia pre -

- ghie - ra ai san - ti ta - ber - na-co-li sa-li. Sem-pre con fè - sin-ce - ra

die - di fio - ri a - gl'al - tar:_____ Nel - l'o - ra del do-lo - re per-

-chè, per-chè, Si-gno - re, per - chè me ne ri - mu - ne-ri co - sì?

Die - di gio - iel - li del-la Ma-don-na al man - to, e die - di il

can - to a - gli a-stri, al ciel, che ne ri-de-an più bel - li. Nel -

102

-l'o - ra del do-lor   per - chè,   per - chè._____ Si -

- gnor,   ah,_____ per-chè me ne ri-mu - ne - ri   co -

- sì?

WISHING YOU WERE SOMEHOW HERE AGAIN

(FROM "THE PHANTOM OF THE OPERA")

Words by Charles Hart. Music by Andrew Lloyd Webber.
Additional Words by Richard Stilgoe.

some-times it seemed if I just dreamed, some-how you would be

here. Wish-ing I could hear your voice a-gain,

know-ing that I ne-ver would, dream-ing of you won't

help me to do all that I dreamed I could.

105

Three long years I knelt in si-lence held your mem - ory near me.

Three long years of mur - mured sor-row will-ing you to hear me.

Too ma-ny years fight-ing back tears, why can't the past just die?

106

WALTZ OF MY HEART

(FROM "THE DANCING YEARS")

Words by Christopher Hassall. Music by Ivor Novello.

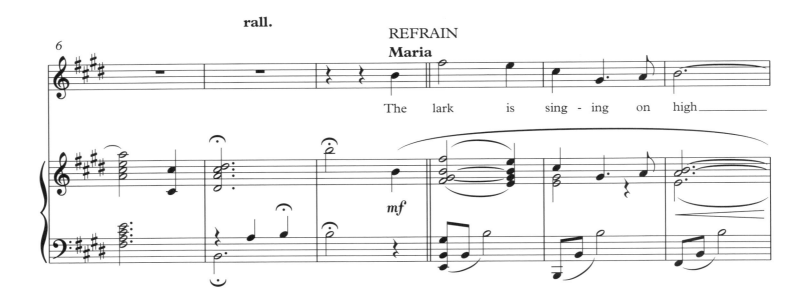

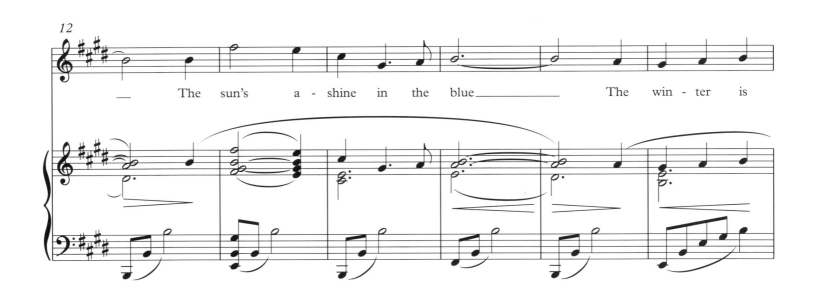

driv - en a - way_____ And spring is re - turn - ing a -

- new._____ Who cares what sor - row may bring_____

What storms may tear us a - part?_____ No sad - ness can

kill The won - der and thrill of that waltz in my

heart.　　　Waltz of my heart,　　　haunt - ing and gay.

Call - ing en - thrall - ing - ly waltz - ing a - way.　　**allarg.**　Ring out your

a tempo bells for me, i - vo - ry keys . . .　　**allarg.** weave out your spells for me　**a tempo**

or - ches - tra　please!　**rall.**　**a tempo** Cho - rus of wings

thril - ling the sky, while you're in - spir - ing me time hur - ries

by. Joy fans a fire in me soon as you start

sweep - ing your strings, waltz of my heart._____ The

lark is sing - ing on high._____ The sun's a - shine in the

blue._____ The win - ter is driv - en a - way_____

and spring is re - turn - ing a - new._____ Who

cares what sor - row may bring_____ What storms may tear us a-

- part?_____ No sad - ness can kill the won - der and

thrill of that waltz in my heart.___

No sad - ness can kill the won - der and

thrill of that waltz in my heart.___

Voi, che sapete
(from "The Marriage of Figaro")

Words by Lorenzo Da Ponte. Music by Wolfgang Amadeus Mozart.

Andante con moto

(*Susanna plays the Ritornello on the guitar.*)

Cherubino

Voi, che sa - pe - te che co - sa è a - mor,

Don - ne, ve - de - te, s'io l'ho nel cor,

Don - ne, ve - de - te,___ s'io l'ho___ nel___ cor.

Quel - lo ch'io pro - vo, vi___ ri - di - rò,___

È per me nuo - vo ca - pir nol so.

Sen - to un af - fet - to pien di de - sir,___

Ch'o - ra è di - let - to, ch'o - ra è mar - tir.

Ge - lo, e poi sen - to l'al - ma av - vam - par.

E in___ un mo - men - to___ tor - no a ge - lar.

Ri - cer - co un be - ne fuo - ri di me,

che co - sa è a-mor, Don - ne, ve - de - te,

s'io l'ho nel cor. Don - ne, ve - de - te,____

s'io l'ho nel cor, Don - ne, ve - de - te,____

s'io l'ho___ nel___ cor.

VOCAL MUSIC

THE BEST OPERA ALBUM IN THE WORLD... EVER!
A selection of best-known arias from opera's greatest masterpieces for high voice and piano accompaniment.
NOV170362

WEST END SHOWSTOPPERS
Twenty sensational songs for voice and piano from the most popular West End musicals.
AM71986

HOW GREAT THOU ART
Twenty-five of the most famous hymns ever written. Including 'The Lord Is My Shepherd' and 'The Old Rugged Cross'
AM61706

THE FIRST BOOK OF SOPRANO SOLOS
These books contain a vaired selection of songs for soprano, arranged in a progressive order.
Part 1 GS81173
Part 2 GS82064

AUDITION SONGS FOR FEMALE SINGERS
A unique CD music pack designed for singers autioning for shows and bands. Containing full backing tracks for each song on the CD.
Book 1 AM92587
Book 2 AM950224

SONGS OF SPAIN VOLUMES 1 & 2
A colletion of songs for high voice from some of Spain's finest composers.
Volume 1 UMV24032
Volume 2 UMV24040

THE CHESTER BOOK OF CELEBRATED SONGS
A varied selected of songs, graded especially for use by singing teachers, students and perforrmers. Includes works by Lully, Dvorak, Schubert and Handel.

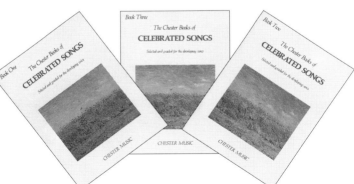

Book 1 CH55317
for High/Med voice & Piano

Book 2 CH55318
for High/Med voice & Piano

Book 3 CH55319
for High/Med voice & Piano

available from Music Sales

MUSIC SALES LIMITED
Sales & Distribution Centre
Newmarket Road, Bury St Edmunds,
Suffolk IP33 3YB
01284 702600